Contents

Notes for parents and other helpers

Welcome to this book

This reading record is made specially for you to fill in yourself. One of your parents or another adult will help you, and so will your teacher. Please read and think about the points below before you start using the book.

Looking after your reading record

- Write your name on the inside front cover, in the space provided. On the lines below your name, copy down carefully your school address, postcode and phone number. If your book gets lost, it can then be returned to you.

- Look after this book carefully and it will last many months. Keep it with your school reading book. You may have a zip wallet or bag to keep both books safe on the journey between home and school.

- Wash your hands before you start reading, to keep dirt and germs away from the book. You can wipe most book covers clean if necessary.

Using this book when you read at home

- Try to read every day with an adult. You can take turns at reading. Enjoy the time together.

- On pages 4 to 23 there is space to make notes on each of your reading sessions. You can write down the date, the book title and the pages you read. In the 'Easy to read?' column, record how your reading went. For example, you could draw a smiley face, or put a tick, or give yourself marks out of 10. The first time you use this book, write your notes at the top of page 4. Then write each new entry below the last one.

- About twice a week, ask an adult who has read with you to write a comment in your reading record. There are some notes for adults on pages 30 and 31.

Make sure that your reading books are kept clean and return them to school in good condition for another child to use.

Focusing on sounds and words

Letter sounds

- Your teacher will show you how to write letter sounds, and you can list them on page 24. These sounds may be useful for word games, rhymes, spelling – and handwriting practice too. Learning letter sounds to help you with reading is sometimes known as phonics.

Target words

- The target words on pages 25 to 27 are for you to practise with an adult when you are in Years 4 and 5. If you can find a word in your reading book and read it correctly, tick 'In context'. When you can read and say a word straight from the list, without any clues, tick 'On sight'.
- You can practise some of the target words by making word cards and playing games with them. Try to use in your own writing any new words that you have learned.

Words about reading

- In Key Stage 2 you learn lots of words about reading. Some of these are listed on pages 28 and 29. You can ask an adult to read these to you. Discuss the meaning of each word, or ask the adult to explain it to you. Enjoy using the words as you talk about reading and books.

Reading targets

- Your teacher may give you reading targets and these may be written on page 32. Always practise as your teacher tells you to. Ask an adult to record the date and comment on how you get on.

You will soon find that you have lots of new achievements to celebrate and these will help you to enjoy reading more and more.

Well done, and happy reading!

My reading record

Date	Title of book	Type of book (for example, fiction, non-fiction, play, legend, folk tale, adventure, poetry, fantasy, humour, biography, mystery)
15.4.14	The wizards promise	Fantasy
19.4.14	Anne of Green Gables	Fiction

Pages read	Easy to read?	Who I read to	Adult's comments
226 39			

Date	Title of book	Type of book

Pages read	Easy to read?	Who I read to	Adult's comments

Date	Title of book	Type of book

Pages read	Easy to read?	Who I read to	Adult's comments

Date	Title of book	Type of book

Pages read	Easy to read?	Who I read to	Adult's comments

Date	Title of book	Type of book

Pages read	Easy to read?	Who I read to	Adult's comments

Date	Title of book	Type of book

Pages read	Easy to read?	Who I read to	Adult's comments

Date	Title of book	Type of book

Pages read	Easy to read?	Who I read to	Adult's comments

Date	Title of book	Type of book

Pages read	Easy to read?	Who I read to	Adult's comments

Date	Title of book	Type of book

Pages read	Easy to read?	Who I read to	Adult's comments

Date	Title of book	Type of book

Pages read	Easy to read?	Who I read to	Adult's comments

Letter sounds

Sound	Sound	Sound	Sound

Target words

Word	In context	On sight
above	▩	▩
across	▩	▩
almost	▩	▩
along	▩	▩
also	▩	▩
always	▩	▩
animals	▩	▩
any	▩	▩
around	▩	▩
asked	▩	▩
baby	▩	▩
balloon	▩	▩
before	▩	▩
began	▩	▩
being	▩	▩
below	▩	▩
better	▩	▩
between	▩	▩
birds	▩	▩
birthday	▩	▩
both	▩	▩
brother	▩	▩

Word	In context	On sight
brought	▩	▩
can't	▩	▩
change	▩	▩
children	▩	▩
clothes	▩	▩
cold	▩	▩
coming	▩	▩
didn't	▩	▩
different	▩	▩
does	▩	▩
don't	▩	▩
dragon	▩	▩
duck	▩	▩
during	▩	▩
earth	▩	▩
every	▩	▩
eyes	▩	▩
father	▩	▩
first	▩	▩
fly	▩	▩
follow(ing)	▩	▩
found	▩	▩

Word	In context	On sight
friends	▨	▨
garden	▨	▨
giant	▨	▨
goes	▨	▨
gone	▨	▨
great	▨	▨
grow	▨	▨
half	▨	▨
happy	▨	▨
head	▨	▨
he's	▨	▨
high	▨	▨
horse	▨	▨
I'm	▨	▨
important	▨	▨
inside	▨	▨
jumped	▨	▨
knew	▨	▨
know	▨	▨
lady	▨	▨
leave	▨	▨
light	▨	▨
liked	▨	▨

Word	In context	On sight
lived	▨	▨
looks	▨	▨
might	▨	▨
money	▨	▨
morning	▨	▨
mother	▨	▨
much	▨	▨
near	▨	▨
never	▨	▨
number	▨	▨
often	▨	▨
only	▨	▨
opened	▨	▨
other	▨	▨
outside	▨	▨
own	▨	▨
paper	▨	▨
park	▨	▨
place	▨	▨
plants	▨	▨
pulled	▨	▨
rabbit	▨	▨
right	▨	▨

a b c d e f g **h i j k l m n** o p **q** r s t u v w x y z

Word	In context	On sight	Word	In context	On sight
river	☐	☐	tries	☐	☐
round	☐	☐	turn(ed)	☐	☐
second	☐	☐	under	☐	☐
show	☐	☐	until	☐	☐
sister	☐	☐	upon	☐	☐
small	☐	☐	used	☐	☐
something	☐	☐	walk(ed)(ing)	☐	☐
sometimes	☐	☐	watch	☐	☐
sound	☐	☐	we're	☐	☐
started	☐	☐	where	☐	☐
still	☐	☐	while	☐	☐
stopped	☐	☐	white	☐	☐
such	☐	☐	whole	☐	☐
suddenly	☐	☐	why	☐	☐
sure	☐	☐	window	☐	☐
swimming	☐	☐	without	☐	☐
think	☐	☐	woke(n)	☐	☐
those	☐	☐	word	☐	☐
thought	☐	☐	work	☐	☐
through	☐	☐	world	☐	☐
today	☐	☐	write	☐	☐
together	☐	☐	year	☐	☐
told	☐	☐	young	☐	☐

Words about reading

Year 3

adjective	encyclopaedia	parable
alliteration	fable	pronoun
apostrophe	grammar	sequel
audience	legend	sequence
bibliography	myth	thesaurus
bullet points	noun	traditional story
dialogue	onomatopoeia	verb

Year 4

abbreviate	discussion	jingle
adverb	editorial	monologue
argument	font	narrative
chorus	epitaph	paragraph
clause	free verse	pun
colon	homophone	simile
debate	hyphen	semi-colon

If you are unsure of the meaning of any of these words,
ask the teacher or look them up in a dictionary.

Year 5

acronym	imagery	resolution
ballad	imperative verb	slang
cliché	metaphor	sonnet
chronological sequence	novel	speech: direct, reported
dialect	point of view	stage direction
edit	preposition	Standard English
extract	quotation	subject
idiom	rhetorical question	technical vocabulary

Year 6

anecdote	journalistic writing	parody
appendix, appendices	hypothesis	personification
asterisk	impersonal language	proverb
autobiography	kenning	riddle
biography	limerick	synopsis
commentary	narrator	viewpoint
complex sentence	obituary	voice
footnote	parenthesis	word derivation

Reading at home

When?

Help your child to enjoy reading each day by making it part of the family routine. A short daily session without distractions is better than an occasional long one. Your child's achievements in both reading and record keeping will soon become apparent.

Where?

Find a comfortable place where you and the child can enjoy reading together. Switch off the TV and ask other family members to be quiet for a few minutes. Keep favourite books in a place where they can easily be found and visit the library and bookshops to look at other reading material.

With whom?

Reading time is quality time for whoever is involved. There is no need for your child to read with the same adult every day. By talking with different family members or friends about his or her reading, your child will learn to enjoy a range of books. By understanding their own likes and dislikes and discussing them, children learn to respect the preferences of others.

How?

Help your child to enjoy reading by encouraging good expression and by discussing the content (see green box, above right, for some suggestions). Support other reading opportunities such as those offered by posters, word books, word games (I spy, Scrabble), computer software, CD-ROMs, read-along story CDs and tapes, hand-held electronic spellcheckers and activity books that are matched to your child's interests and help with group work in school.

Discussing a book with your child

First, talk about the title, the author's name and the type of book (genre). Then discuss any links that the subject matter may have with events that the child has experienced. If the book is fiction, discuss the setting, plot (what happens), main character and favourite characters. If the book is non-fiction, ask: What have you learned? Is the subject explained clearly? What do you notice about the layout of the book? Are the pictures and diagrams helpful?

Why?

This book will help encourage your child to establish a regular habit of reading and record keeping. Make full use of the reading record to focus on your child's progress and give praise at every opportunity.

Keep reading to your child even after he or she has learned to read independently.

Help your child to read his or her name, home address and telephone number. For security reasons we do not encourage children to write these details in this book: however, your child does need to know them.

Using this book

Use this book to keep a record of your child's reading. Your child will take some responsibility for record keeping. Please supervise this at least twice a week. Allow your child to tick boxes, write comments and add stickers or smiley faces. The teacher will need to see the book daily, so make sure that your child takes it to school.

Reading record (pages 4 to 23)

This is a record of what your child reads and when. Here you can add positive comments on his or her reading and note tricky words that the child might practise. If you have been able to help your child read for a day or two, make a note of this too. Here are some examples of other comments you might make:

We took it in turns to read the pages.
We discussed what might happen next.
We are going to practise the rhyming words, for fun.
Very good expression. Well done!
This week we chose some books at the library.
Very clear independent reading today.
He has lots of background knowledge of this subject so we had a discussion instead of reading aloud.
We are looking again at this book to check the main points.
We'll watch the video of this story at the weekend to help with understanding.

Letter sounds (page 24)

Here the teacher can list the letter sounds that your child is learning in school. Ask the teacher to explain the phonics system if it is new to you or your child.

Target words (pages 25 to 27)

If the child can find the word in a reading book and read it correctly, tick 'In context'. If the child can read a selected word straight from the list, with no clues, tick 'On sight'.

Words about reading (pages 28 and 29)

The terms listed here will form part of your child's developing vocabulary. Encourage him or her to read and use them correctly. If you are unsure of the meaning of any words, ask the teacher or consult a dictionary.

Reading targets (page 32)

The targets page is at the back of this book, for quick reference. Here the teacher can list your child's individual reading targets, and you can discuss these at parent–teacher meetings. As you check the targets and regularly report on your child's reading progress, the reading record will help to ensure effective home–school communication.

Reading targets

Date set	Target	Date met